THE MAN
THE BOY
AND THE DONKEY

THE MAN
THE BOY
AND THE DONKEY

RETOLD BY KATHERINE EVANS

Illustrated by the Author

ALBERT WHITMAN & COMPANY · CHICAGO

Published Simultaneously in
The Dominion of Canada by
George J. McLeod Ltd., Toronto

© Copyright 1958
L.C. Card 58-12316
Lithographed in the
United States of America

THE MAN, THE BOY,
AND THE DONKEY

One day Papa Bon said to
Mama Bon, "Today I will sell
our donkey at the Fair."
Mama Bon said to Papa Bon,
"Be sure to get a good price
for him."

Little Peter said, "Papa,
please take me."
"You may go with me,"
said Papa Bon.

So Papa Bon and Peter
set out for town to sell
their donkey at the Fair.
Peter walked on one side of
the little donkey and Papa Bon
on the other.

They went down the hill and
up the road. They met some
girls returning from the Fair.

"Look," cried one of the girls. "How silly to walk when they could be riding on the donkey."

They laughed so hard
that Papa Bon said,
"Peter, you ride
on the donkey's back
and I will walk."
So Peter rode on the
donkey's back and Papa Bon
walked beside him.

Farther down the road
they passed two old men.

"There," said one of them,
"Do you see that lazy boy
riding while his father
has to walk?"
"Get down, you good-for-nothing
boy and let the man ride,"
they said.

After this Papa Bon said,
"Peter, you get down and
I will ride the donkey."
Just as they came to the town
they saw some women and
children.

"Look at that lazy fellow,"
they all cried.
"How can he ride on the
donkey when that poor little boy
can hardly keep up with him?"

"Peter," said Papa Bon,
"We will both ride on the donkey.
Then everyone will be happy."

The little donkey trotted
into town with Papa Bon
and Peter on his back.

"Is that your donkey?" asked
a man on the street.
"Yes," said Papa Bon.

"Well, I am surprised you load him so heavily. Why, you two could more easily carry the poor little donkey than he can carry you."

Papa Bon did not want to go
through the town and
have people see the donkey
with such a heavy load.

So he and Peter got down
from the donkey. Papa Bon said,
"We will carry the donkey. You
must try to carry his shoulders.
I will carry his back legs."

They puffed and grunted
and at last they lifted the
donkey up to their shoulders.
They started across a little bridge
that led to the fair grounds.

People ran after them.
They laughed and laughed.
It was such a strange sight to see
a donkey being carried.

"Look at that silly donkey!"
they said.

No one at the Fair would buy
a donkey that had to be carried.

So Peter and Papa Bon
made their way home
without selling their donkey.
They were very sad.

As they went past the village
and up the hill, Papa Bon
said to Peter,
"Next time we take the donkey
to the Fair we will remember,
if you try to please every one
you please no one."